WAX
IN OUR WORLD

SOLVEIG PAULSON RUSSELL

Illustrated by PAULA HUTCHISON

Rand McNally & Company

CHICAGO · NEW YORK · SAN FRANCISCO

TO FRANCES STARR

Who has an understanding heart

CONTENTS

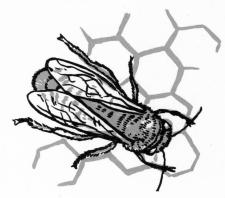

Figures from Madame Tussaud's, one of which is getting finishing touches from a waxworks assistant

Wax for the Arts

PEOPLE OF WAX ✦✦✦✦

There is a place in London, England—Madame Tussaud's—where many historical figures are on display. There are more than ninety exhibits of individuals or groups of famous people, including kings and queens, military men, and statesmen of many countries. There are American presidents: among them Washington, Lincoln, Theodore Roosevelt, Hoover, Franklin D. Roosevelt, and Eisenhower. There are other Americans such as Joe Louis, Danny Kaye, and Mark Twain, along with Queen Elizabeth, Princess Margaret, members of their family, and other famous people from all over the world. There is even a "Chamber of Horrors," containing notorious criminals.

These people are not real; they are made of wax. But the thousands of visitors who have been looking at Madame Tussaud's figures for more than 100 years have exclaimed over and over, "They look so real!" They do, for each is carefully dressed in the clothes of his time—often in clothes that really belonged to him—and each one is perfectly formed, with every detail of features and coloring exactly as it was in life. Even warts and scars are there. Some policemen among the exhibits, for example, seem so real that people often stop to ask directions from them.

Madame Tussaud, who started the famous museum in 1854, learned to model figures in wax when she was just a child in France. When she grew up, she established the museum in England and continually added more figures as time passed, and as her fame grew. Members of her family have carried on the work through the years. Each year a few figures are added to the collection—people who have been in the news frequently, and who are likely to be remembered for a long time.

There are also a number of wax museums in America. One is the National Historical Wax Museum in Washing-

Betsy Ross, in National Historical Wax Museum, Washington, D. C.

Assassination of Abraham Lincoln, also in Washington Museum

ton, D.C. Others are in Gettysburg, Pennsylvania; in St. Augustine and North Miami Beach, in Florida; in Scottsdale, Arizona; in Buena Park, California; and in New York City. In each one figures are shown that startle those who see them because they look so alive. No other material can be colored and shaped to resemble flesh so well as the beeswax used for the models in these museums.

The National Historical Wax Museum of Washington, D.C. opened in 1958. The models are arranged to show famous events of American history. In one scene an Indian is about to hit John Smith of Jamestown on the head with a tomahawk. Other scenes show Betsy Ross sewing our first flag, the signing of the Declaration of Independence, the Wright Brothers' old bicycle shop, where they planned their first airplane, and the Yalta Conference with Franklin Roosevelt, Josef Stalin, and Winston Churchill looking very lifelike. Many other landmarks in American history are depicted, including up-to-date space flying.

In Gettysburg, the National Civil War Wax Museum opened in 1962. It contains settings and figures from the Civil War, and uses sound tracks and light to help create a feeling of reality. There one may see, among other scenes, Lincoln and Douglas as they looked while debating; the great nurse Clara Barton, at Antietam; Generals Lee and Grant at Appomattox; and the assassination of Lincoln.

Potter's Wax Museum was opened in 1951 in St. Augustine. It contains groups of composers, writers, statesmen,

Christopher Columbus and his son, in Spain (Miami Wax Museum)

royalty, and American leaders such as Franklin, Jefferson, Webster, and Grant.

The Wax Museum in North Miami Beach, Florida, started showing its tableaux of historical figures in 1959. There one may look back into the early history of Florida. One may see Columbus seeking help in Spain for his first voyage to the New World; the aging Ponce de Leon as he discovered Florida; and scenes with early Indians and Spanish explorers. Fighting at the Alamo and the Boston Tea Party are among other historical settings shown. Recorded voices tell the story of each scene when a button near it is pressed.

The American Heritage Wax Museum is in Scottsdale, Arizona. It opened in 1962. There are wax figures in this museum of a number of presidents, statesmen, authors, and inventors; but the "Heroes of the West" are the chief attraction. Here figures of Wild Bill Hickok, Annie Oakley, Buffalo Bill, Calamity Jane, Jesse James, Wyatt Earp, Doc Holliday, Sitting Bull, and other famous Westerners, can be seen as they were in the days when the West was wild.

Moviland Wax Museum at Buena Park, California, also opened in 1962. It shows wax figures of movieland's famous actors and actresses of the past and present.

WAX AND ANCIENT BELIEFS ✦✦✦✦

Skilfully made wax figures have been discovered in Egyptian tombs, and it is known that these were created centuries before Christ was born.

The ancient Egyptians believed in a life after death, and prepared lavishly for it. They believed that this life took place in a spirit world. But they thought spirits needed the remains of their earthly bodies in a life after death and that their bodies had to be preserved exactly as they were on earth. Otherwise, they believed, they could not remain in the spirit world.

That is why they arranged to have their bodies specially treated after death, and placed into beautiful coffins. We call these preserved bodies mummies, and wax was used in preparing the mummies. Often, however, they went a step further, in case their real bodies should be destroyed in some way after all. They had an artist make images of their bodies from wax or clay. They believed the images could serve in place of the real body if necessary. Many of these little images have been found, lying in small coffins just like the larger ones in which the real dead bodies had been placed. If the image was of wax, it was usually beeswax.

In Egypt, Babylonia, India and, later, in Greece and Rome, some people believed that wax models of living persons had magical powers. They hired witches and wizards to make wax models of their enemies. Then they misused and hurt the models, thinking that this would bring bad luck to the real people the models represented.

The Mayan Indians of Central America had the same belief, but they also used wax in healing the sick. Their magicians made wax moldings of the part of the body that needed healing. Then they burned or buried the wax figures, believing that would work a cure. What they thought, when they were not healed, no one can say.

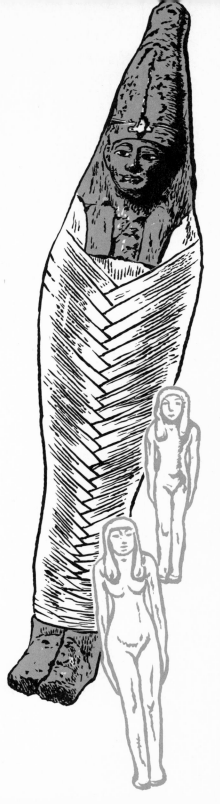

The gilded wax mask of a mummy, and two small wax figurines from an Egyptian tomb

Wax and Sculpture ✦✦✦✦

Sculptors have frequently used wax to aid them in their work. Wax is useful to them because it is so easily modeled. When slightly warm, it can be rolled, pinched, twisted, stretched, bent, and shaped in any way. Mistakes can be easily corrected and the form reshaped. New pieces of wax can be joined to older ones by applying a little pressure. Very fine lines and designs can be made in wax with simple tools, such as sharpened slender wood or metal rods.

Many famous artists made small models of wax to serve as patterns for final work in stone and metal. Often, if a piece of sculpture had been ordered from the artist, the buyer first approved a small wax model before the artist started the larger permanent work.

Michelangelo and Leonardo da Vinci were among the great artists who made wax models of their work. Edgar Degas was a French painter of the nineteenth century, especially well known for his lovely paintings of ballet dancers. When he became so old that he could no longer see well enough to paint, he modeled wax figures that he could feel.

Patience Lovell Wright, an American sculptress of the eighteenth century, worked only in wax, as Madame Tussaud did.

Gainsborough, one of the most famous of English portrait painters, carved heads from candle ends for fun.

Near the end of the eighteenth century, a man named

Vase and figurines of Wedgwood

John Flaxman carved small portraits and other figures in wax, which were then cast in clay by Josiah Wedgwood, who used them as decorations for the beautiful pottery that still bears his name.

WAX FOR CASTING METAL ❖❖❖❖

Wax was also used for making molds to be cast in gold and other metals—silver, tin, copper, and bronze. The very earliest metalwork was cast in wax molds.

It often happened, in the days when communications between different parts of the world did not exist, that the same discoveries were made at about the same time, oceans apart. This was true of the use of wax as casts for metalwork. Before the Spaniards came to America, the Aztecs, the Toltecs, and other Indians were skilled in the use of wax for casting gold and silver into beautiful ornaments and art objects, such as vases and figures of their gods.

In China, India, Africa, Egypt, and parts of our own continent, the casting of metal in wax was developed at about the same time. The process was approximately the same everywhere and remains the same today.

The casting process is now called the *Cire Perdu,* or "Lost Wax" process. It has this name because the wax used is run out of the mold, or "lost" in the casting process. For the making of a small casting, the object was first carved in wax, with as much fine detail as the maker wished to include. A moist clay shell was then pressed against the wax. A funnel-shaped opening was made at the top through the clay.

When the clay was thoroughly dry and hard, the object was heated. The wax carving inside the clay shell melted, and the wax ran out through the hole at the top, when the shell was turned upside down. By this time the inside of the clay shell was marked with the design that had been carved on the wax. Then the metal, or combination of metals—gold, silver, brass, bronze, etc.—was melted and poured through the funnel hole into the space where the wax had been, filling every indentation on the inside of the clay. When the metal was cold and set, the clay covering was broken and removed, and the form that had been carved in wax appeared, duplicated in every detail in metal.

Metal expands under high heat and cracks, so if large figures were to be molded they had to be left hollow on the

Nowadays, more complicated methods are used

1. An object is carved in wax
2. A moist clay shell is pressed around the object, and a funnel-like opening is made at the top
3. When it is hard, the clay is baked

16

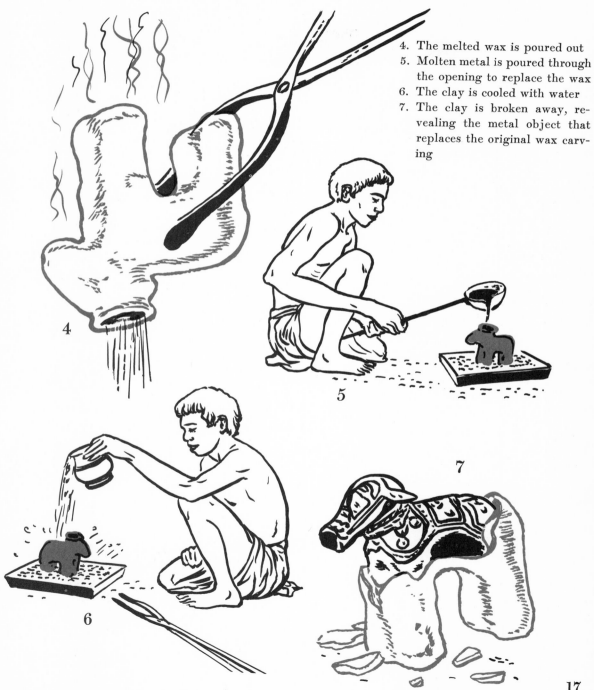

4. The melted wax is poured out
5. Molten metal is poured through the opening to replace the wax
6. The clay is cooled with water
7. The clay is broken away, revealing the metal object that replaces the original wax carving

inside. This was done by making a core in the general shape of the object to be cast, of a material such as broken brick or plaster, or charcoal and clay worked together. Then wax was put over the core, and the artist worked it just as he had done for the smaller object without a core.

When the wax model was finished, it was covered with layers of wet clay or plaster. Metal pins were passed through this clay or plaster into the core, so that when the wax was melted and ran out, the core would stay in place.

A wax funnel was placed at the bottom of the outer coat of the mold. When the clay or plaster shell was hard, the mold was heated as before, and the melted wax ran out. Then the mold was inverted and metal was poured in, through the hole left by the wax funnel.

When the metal was cold, the outer surface and the metal pins were broken off, and the inner core was taken out, leaving a hollow metal casting exactly like the wax model.

The "Lost Wax" process is still used, with some improvements. It can be used for the most delicate jewelry as well as for huge bronze monuments. But it is also used in industry where the basic process is still the same.

During World War II, ways of using this process were developed to speed up the making of machine parts. Engineers designed complicated parts that were needed for new and improved planes and the implements of war. These parts were difficult to make with ordinary machinery and by forging. Manufacturers found that they could be more quickly made by the "Lost Wax" process. After the war, peacetime use of the wax-casting process continued. It is now used for making many complicated parts for different kinds of machines, for zippers, camera parts, and the like.

WAX FOR WRITING AND PAINTING ✷✷✷✷

Long before anyone had paper, the Egyptians made writing tablets out of wax. They scraped a shallow rectangular area out of both sides of a piece of wood, leaving a narrow

The Lost Wax process is now used for a large variety of objects

raised edge. Then they poured dark melted wax into the parts they had scraped out which, when cool, left a sheet of smooth wax on each side of the board.

With a stylus, the Egyptians could write on the wax, scratching through the dark wax so that the lighter wood of the tablet made the writing clear. Usually a stylus was made of metal or bone. One end was sharp for writing. The other end of the stylus had a rounded knob, or a flat surface, for smoothing wax when mistakes were made. When they wanted to use their wax tablets over again, the Egyptians smoothed the wax, filling in the marks they had made. Later, wax tablets were also made in Greece and Rome.

The Egyptians also invented a way of painting with wax. They mixed colors into melted wax and poured it into small cylinders to cool. Then they took up bits of colored wax with heated spatulas and decorated mummy

Egyptian scribe, wax tablet, and stylus

Egyptian boat and decorations

cases, walls and furniture, and made portraits. Sometimes they did their painting with brushes and the melted wax paint, letting the wax set on the decorated object. This method was used for decorating ships. Wax paint was waterproof.

Wax painting is called encaustic painting.

After oil paint was developed, encaustic painting was no longer popular, because oil paints were much easier to use and could be better controlled.

In the island of Java, however, wax painting is still done. We call this work "batik." It is a way of making beautiful patterns on cloth. Batik work is also done in a small way in other places, but it is an important art in Java.

The Javanese usually work with cotton cloth, but sometimes they use silk. The cotton material is first prepared by repeated washing and soaking to remove the lime that is contained in cotton. When it is dry, it is hung on frames. The artist then quickly traces a design on the cloth with melted wax, which is kept warm in a small vessel placed over a little hearth.

When the design has been painted on the cloth, and the wax has hardened, the cloth is dipped in a dye bath. Only the parts of the cloth that contain no wax pick up the dye, because the waterproof wax protects the parts it covers from the liquid dye.

When the cloth is dry, the artist scrapes off the first

Batik work. The tool used is called a tjanting

wax, applies it again where she wishes to protect the cloth from another color, and then dips it into a different dye. When this process has been repeated a number of times with different colors, the cotton or silk is quite beautiful, with its colorful designs.

Some textile manufacturers use a batik method of printing cloth by machine that is similar to the hand method. They cover parts of the cloth with a layer of wax before dying it, but the results are not as elaborate or unusual as batik done by hand.

Wax and Printing ❖❖❖❖

One method of printing depends on the use of wax. The story goes that its inventor, Alois Senefelder, was once asked to write down a laundry list for his mother. Not having any paper at hand at the moment, he grabbed up a piece of wax or wax crayon and wrote the list on a flat, porous stone.

Senefelder was a printer in Bavaria and he was constantly experimenting with inks, acids, and printing plates. For some reason, he decided to experiment with the stone on which he had written the laundry list. He moistened the stone with diluted acid. Then he rolled ink over the acid, and put a piece of paper down on the ink. When the paper was removed, Senefelder saw that he had an exact reproduction of the list he had written with wax. His ink had stuck to the wax, which had not been affected by the acid bath because it was water-repellent. The ink had not remained on the wet surfaces of stone where there was no wax.

This method of printing is known as lithography. Originally, lithography was done by hand and was used by artists who wanted more than one copy of a painting. The method was similar to batik work in that the process had to be repeated for each color. Since then lithography has be-

Alois Senefelder and his crude lithography press

come of great importance to the printing industry. Metal plates—usually zinc or aluminum—are used instead of stone and these are placed on a printing press. Various kinds of printing inks have been developed for lithographic printing, but all have a greasy or waxy base. Some artists, however, still do their lithographs on stone to get a special effect.

1. The artist draws on the stone with a black grease crayon; 2. Greasy ink is rolled over the stone with a wooden roller covered with horsehide; 3. A print is pulled from the stone

Wax for Everyday Life

To Provide Light ✦✦✦✦

It is hard to imagine a time when the only light that could push away the darkness was firelight. Yet for many centuries early men had no other means of seeing in the dark. From their burning fires they made torches of branches or long sticks with pitchy knots on them. Sometimes they dipped the ends of their torches in animal fat or beeswax to make them burn brighter.

Gradually, as time passed, men saw that torches could be improved. They could be made of thinner splints, bound at the tip with leaves in which charcoal and fats were wrapped together. They could be fashioned of reeds and rushes bound together, with the tips coated with materials that burned easily, such as resin or animal fat. And they could be made so that they burned with less smoke.

After men had used torches for a long time they learned that if a bit of twisted moss or other plant fibers was put in fat the fiber would draw the fat into itself and burn from the end. These fibers were called wicks. The first lamps were shells, or rocks with hollows in them, used as

Early torches and lamps

containers in which to burn fats with a lighted wick. Later metal lamps were made.

But these early ways of lighting were not as effective as the candle. Although authorities do not agree as to when candles of wax were first used, they were probably first made in Rome. A Roman writer, Pliny, tells of the making of candles. Some were made of flax thread, covered with wax and pitch; others used a wick of papyrus fibers that was dipped in beeswax or tallow—a kind of animal fat.

Lanthorn

Skill in candlemaking developed and became more important as time passed. From the Romans it spread to England and France. In 848 A.D., King Alfred of England made a lantern (lanthorn) by enclosing a candle in a box made of transparent sheets of horn.

In the Middle Ages, beeswax was very important. Much of it was used for church candles. The demand was so great that beeswax was sometimes used in place of money, and presents and legacies of it were common. Only the church and the wealthy people could afford to use beeswax candles.

Other waxes and tallow were also used for candles. The Chinese used a wax they got from insects, and other peoples used the natural waxes they had. These included wax from palm leaves, reeds, and shrubs such as the candelilla of Mexico. But tallow and beeswax were used in

Early candle holder, with bayberry candle

Europe and in the United States until sperm wax from whales and paraffin from petroleum were introduced.

Sperm wax came into use in the last part of the eighteenth century and paraffin in the middle of the nineteenth. In the United States, our early settlers also used wax from bayberry plants for candles. They boiled the waxy berries of the plant in water and skimmed off the wax that rose to the top of the water.

Candles are made by repeatedly dipping wicks into melted wax or tallow until the dippings build up to form the candles, or by pouring melted wax into molds containing central wicks. Candles are also now made by machines that feed wicks into pistons filled with melted wax, from which the candles are pushed out when cool.

Although candles are no longer our main source of light, they still have a place in our modern living. When electricity fails, almost every home has a candle or two on hand to dispel the darkness with a soft glow of golden light. Some people eat their meals by candlelight, because the soft light is so pleasant. A great number of candles are made for church use every year.

Thomas Edison's wonderful mind first thought of making an instrument that would react to the vibrations of sound through grooves cut into a cylinder of soft material. His first experiment was with a cylinder wrapped in tinfoil. He recited "Mary had a little lamb" into a tube that had a needle attached to one end to make grooves in the tinfoil as it was turned.

When another needle attached to another tube was played through the grooves "Mary had a little lamb" came back faintly from the machine. Imagine how strange this must have seemed to people who had never dreamed of making recordings of voices. It almost scared them.

Thomas Edison and his phonograph

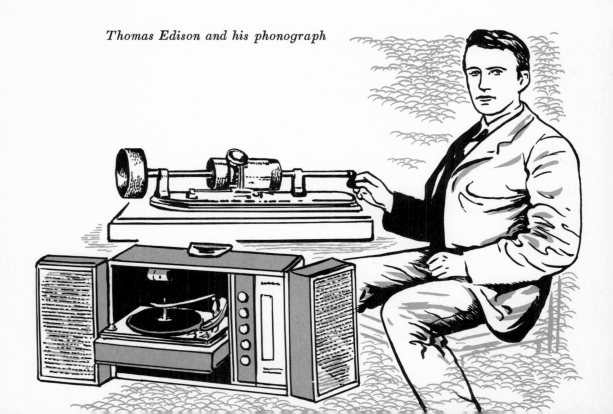

Tinfoil, however, was not good material for recording. It tore easily, so for almost ten years Edison's talking machine was of little value. Then one day he turned his thoughts toward improving it. He knew much about wax, for he had used it often in his electrical experiments.

He made a hollow cylinder of wax to replace the tinfoil. With this on the machine, and a sapphire needle for cutting grooves, a way of making first-class recordings was found.

Now the recording cylinder has been replaced by a flat record disk and the electrical recording and play-backs are much improved. Great numbers of duplicate records can be made from a master record.

To make a master record, a blank wax disk is turned, while sound vibrations are picked up electrically and cut into the wax disk. The cut disk is then coated and hardened by a number of complicated operations to make a metal form. Then mixed melted materials from which records are made—compounds of shellac and minerals—are pressed against the master form by steam-heated presses. When the materials in the form have cooled, the disks are ready to reproduce the master record perfectly.

For Duplicating ✤✤✤✤

Carbon paper is so common these days that we pay little attention to it. But a hundred years ago carbon paper was unknown. Before it was invented, people who needed more than one copy of any writing had to make the necessary copies by hand.

No one knows who made the first carbon paper, but there is a story that a Boston chemist became so disgusted with the mistakes his assistants made in copying his work that he thought up a copy paper so that he could make several copies of his work at one time.

He mixed up grease, tallow, and lampblack carbon and rubbed it on writing paper. This was carbon paper of a sort, but it was messy and dirty. It smudged and smeared, but it could be used for making several copies. A number of companies began to make this kind of carbon paper, at first putting the carbon mixture on by hand, but later doing it with machinery, which was a very dirty job for the workers.

The first carbon paper smeared the clothes and fingers of all office workers who used it, and in a few months the grease in it worked its way through the paper so that the surface became too dry to use. This carbon paper was certainly not satisfactory.

Then, in the early part of our century, a shipment from Brazil of carnauba—a new kind of wax—took care of many carbon paper difficulties. When it was mixed with grease and lampblack and used as a coating on thin paper, it made a copy paper that was clean and hard, and gave sharp copies of the writing done by hand and by the new improved typewriters and office machines of that time.

When carbon black and dye were substituted for the old lampblack, the resulting ink dissolved in the carnauba wax. This changed the formerly thick, smeary ink into a watery state that could be more easily put on paper and made an even, brilliant coating.

Huge amounts of carbon paper are used every day in the business world. The carbon paper manufacturers have developed many new ways of meeting this need. Since overcoming their first problems by using carnauba wax, they have developed many new kinds of ink. These meet the special purposes and needs of the complicated business machines of our time. Now these manufacturers are among the largest users of various kinds of wax.

Huge amounts of carbon paper are used in the business world

Nature protects leaves, flowers, and fruits with a delicate coating of wax. When you look at a leaf or rub an apple, you can see the shine of the wax surface. The wax on cactus plants protects the inner moisture from evaporation in the hot desert sun.

Man also coats some fruits—especially lemons, oranges, limes, and grapefruit—with thin coats of wax to improve their keeping qualities and appearance. The fruits are passed through wax coating baths on endless belts, or chains. From the baths they move through long-haired brushes that polish them.

People who sell plants sometimes dip the plants in melted wax to protect them from drying while they are being shipped.

Nature and man coat fruits, flowers, and plants with wax to preserve them

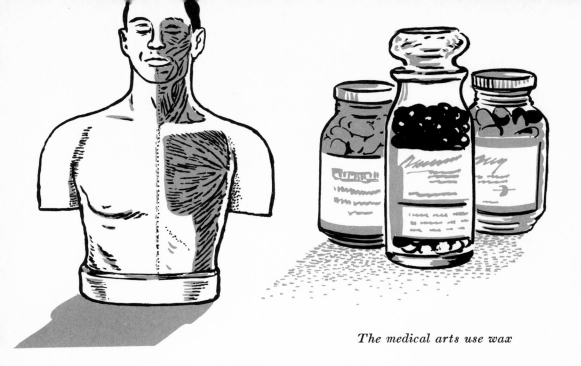

The medical arts use wax

WAX FOR MEDICINE AND COSMETICS ✦✦✦✦

The medical arts use wax. Medical students study realistic models of body parts that are made of wax. Plastic surgeons use it for making models that they can study for their work of restoring or changing people's faces and features. Dentists use it in making impressions for false teeth. Salves and ointments and other medicines contain wax or are contained in wax coverings. The glossy look of some pills is due to wax.

Beauty preparations and cosmetics use tons of wax every year. All kinds of lotions and creams, and other beauty aids for both men and women, are constantly being made and used in great quantities. The cosmetic industry is a huge one.

*Servants skated over the floors to
polish them*

Floors in ancient buildings, which were treated with wax and were probably polished by servants who skated over them with cloth tied to their feet, have remained un-worn for centuries. Wax polish saves the wear on many surfaces, from shoes to furniture.

Even rubber products—such as tires, electrical insula-tors, and hot water bottles—last longer because wax is added to the rubber of which they are made. Wax in rubber helps to protect it against cracking from the action of heat and air. It is sometimes used to soften rubber, and also to give it smoothness.

Wax waterproofs clothing, tent material, and cover-ings of different kinds, protecting them from moisture.

Wax paper is one of the best-known wax products for protecting and preserving. Every day we see it wrapped around bread and other foods. It has thousands of uses.

One common way of making wax paper, in big ma-chines, is to pass lengths of very thin paper over rollers that are partly immersed in melted wax. The rollers pick up the wax and transfer it to the paper. Then the paper passes through squeeze rollers that press the wax into all of the fibers of the paper.

Another way of coating paper with wax is to pass it through baths of melted wax and then draw it from the baths up through heated scrapers that scrape off the excess wax. The paper then passes through rollers that smooth the surface.

Above: Testing the tensile strength of wax paper; Below: Rollers of wax-coating machine apply a layer of wax onto lengths of thin paper

There are many grades of wax paper. Some are more heavily waxed than others. The amount of wax used depends on the kind and temperature of the wax, and on the way it is applied to the paper. Some waxed papers are made with a layer of wax between two thin sheets of unwaxed paper.

Other Uses of Wax ❖❖❖❖

Wax on the outside wrapping of food can easily be seen, but the use of wax in baked foods is not commonly known. Bakers use wax in bread and cake to keep them soft and fresh longer. It is used in frostings and sometimes in the sugar for coating doughnuts. Its use in doughnut sugar makes the doughnuts look fresh longer by keeping the sugar from soaking up grease.

Wax is used to help strengthen the effect of whipping in some foods such as ice cream. And it is used in candies to lessen stickiness. Wax helps keep the flavor of chocolate and makes it shine.

Bakers use wax in bread and cake

Chewing gum is a mixture of various materials, including wax. About three million pounds of wax are used each year by chewing gum makers.

Without wax we would have no crayons, printing inks, china-marking pencils, and paints, as we know them today. Wax is used in all of them, and in magic writing pads, too. Many children know these pads. They are made of dark waxed cardboard with a sheet of cellophane or other clear material over them. When the outer sheet is marked, the marks show through. When the top sheet is lifted, the marks disappear.

Wax is used in some cleaners, such as dustless sweeping mixtures, windshield cleaners, ink-removers, saddle soaps, typewriter cleaners, and hand cleaners.

There are so many uses of wax, and products that depend on it, that it has been said we live on a film of wax. This is true, for we walk on it, clean with it, wear it, read words made possible through its use, and even eat it. Every day chemists are at work finding new uses for wax, so there is no possibility that its use will grow less.

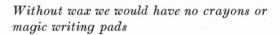

Without wax we would have no crayons or magic writing pads

Kinds of Wax

DEFINITION AND CLASSES OF WAX ❖❖❖❖

Wax is hard to define. Originally the word was used for beeswax only. But now we think of wax as a plastic, slippery solid that is easy to melt. It usually has a shiny surface and feels greasy.

There are four main classes of wax: mineral, vegetable, insect, and marine animal. Some waxes have proved to be best for use in certain products, but a number of waxes can be substituted for others, and have similar uses. Often wax products contain mixtures or blends of different waxes.

MINERAL WAX ❖❖❖❖

Mineral wax is wax that comes from the earth. The mineral waxes are ozokerite, montan, and paraffin.

Ozokerite is a wax that occurs in veins, or deposits, similar to veins of metal in the earth, and it is mined, just as metals are. After mining, it has to be separated from the rocky materials in which it is imbedded. Ozokerite is found in Utah and Texas in the United States, and in Poland, Russia, and Austria.

Geologists—scientists who study the history of the earth through its rocks—believe that ozokerite, or Utah wax—as it is commonly called in the United States—developed from petroleum.

Petroleum was formed millions of years ago when the earth teemed with huge plants and strange animals and fishes, and water and swamps were abundant. As changes occurred in the earth, the land masses rose and buckled, and the huge layers of swampy life were buried and pressed down by tremendous pressure into what is now coal and petroleum.

A vein of ozokorite ore

In the places where ozokerite is found, geologists think that the earth movements left fissures and caverns under the earth's surface, and that, in time, with more earth movements, petroleum was forced up into these empty places. Temperature changes, pressure, and the presence of some kinds of salts and clays changed the character of the petroleum into ozokerite wax.

Ozokerite wax is separated from its ore by different methods. It can be boiled out of the ore or treated with acid. The refining gives several different grades of wax of different colors before it is bleached. The grades differ in brittleness and flexibility.

Montan wax is a hard, lustrous wax that comes from lignite. Lignite occurs in many places on the earth. It is said to be coal in the making. If left untouched it will become coal as more ages pass. It is made by nature from ancient, decayed woody materials; and it is mined from the earth. It is sometimes called brown coal, and is used for burning as coal is used.

All lignite does not contain the same amount of montan wax. Some has very little, some has more. When the lignite is mined, it is crushed and treated with chemicals to free the montan wax.

Paraffin is the third kind of mineral wax. It is a white wax and, like ozokerite, is a product of petroleum, often called black gold. At the refineries paraffin is taken from the black gold in several ways. It is separated from the other products of petroleum by changes in temperature, by

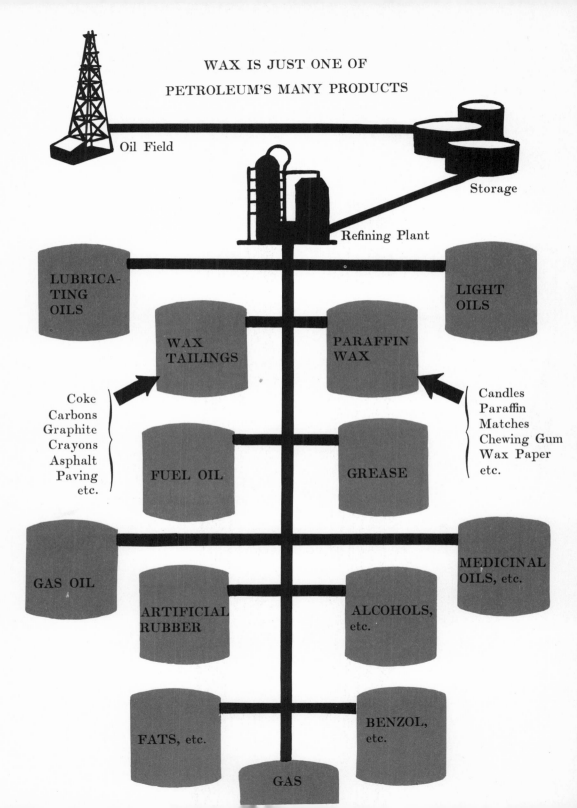

WAX IS JUST ONE OF
PETROLEUM'S MANY PRODUCTS

Oil Field

Storage

Refining Plant

LUBRICA-
TING
OILS

LIGHT
OILS

WAX
TAILINGS

PARAFFIN
WAX

Coke
Carbons
Graphite
Crayons
Asphalt
Paving
etc.

Candles
Paraffin
Matches
Chewing Gum
Wax Paper
etc.

FUEL OIL

GREASE

GAS OIL

MEDICINAL
OILS, etc.

ARTIFICIAL
RUBBER

ALCOHOLS,
etc.

FATS, etc.

BENZOL,
etc.

GAS

filtering, by treating with solvents, and by whirling the oil so that the suspended wax particles will be thrown against the sides of the tanks where they can be removed.

Tons of paraffin are used daily, because it has countless uses. Probably you know it best as a protection for home-made jelly.

Hot melted paraffin is poured over homemade jelly, as soon as jelly is in the jars, to prevent spoilage

The most important vegetable wax in the world, and the hardest and toughest of the natural waxes, grows on palm trees—the carnauba palms of Brazil.

In the land of the carnaubas the rain falls in torrents, flooding and drenching the country. And after the rainy period come scorching days and dry relentless winds that parch the earth. Carnauba palms grow well only in Brazil. Through the rain and through the dry times the carnauba palm rises gracefully and offers her many gifts to the people of the land. Because it is so useful this palm has been called the "Tree of Life."

Cattle feed upon the new leaves, and people eat the palmetto, or heart of the new plant. An extract used for medicine comes from the roots; the sap makes wine and vinegar. The fruit, similar to dates, is fed to animals, and is also made into a drink for people. The seeds are a coffee substitute when toasted and ground. The hard lumber from the trunk is useful for building and for firewood.

From the palm leaves the people make many things— hats, mats, baskets, sacks, brooms, and thatch for their homes. The fibers supply fishing nets, light rope, blankets, and cords. Candles come from the wax that forms on the leaves.

The carnauba palm must be from eight to ten years old before it has enough wax to harvest.

Three or four months after the rainy season ends, natives go out into the forests with their donkeys to har-

The carnauba palm, known as the "Tree of Life" must be from eight to ten years old before it has enough wax to harvest

vest the palm fronds. To reach up and cut the fronds, each man uses a small knife at the end of a long pole. The clippers know just how many leaves they can cut without hurting the tree. When the leaves fall, they are stacked on the donkeys' backs in piles so high the donkeys can scarcely be seen.

After cutting, the leaves are taken to open places in the forest. There they are spread to dry, and are turned a number of times so that the sun and wind dry them thoroughly. When dry they go into threshing sheds where men first pull them over sharp steel teeth set in a v-shaped holder. This action shreds the leaves. Then they are pulled

To cut the fronds, each man uses a small knife at the end of a long pole

apart fanwise, and, finally, they are gathered into bundles and beaten across wood to shake out the wax.

The fine wax showers from the leaves in powdery scales. When enough has been shaken off, it is gathered up and put into bags. Sometimes it is melted at the threshing places and made into blocks for shipping.

Carnauba wax is refined by melting, filtering, and boiling.

Carnauba trees are slow growing, but live up to two hundred years. A mature tree gives only five or six ounces of wax per year. When we know that millions of pounds of carnauba wax are used every year, we can appreciate the

When the leaves fall, they are stacked on the donkeys' backs in high piles

Candelilla wax comes from a Mexican plant

great number of Brazilian trees that are needed to meet this demand.

Another wax tree of Brazil is the ouricury wax palm. Its wax is similar to carnauba wax in some ways, but it cannot be shaken from the leaves in drifting wax flakes. The ouricury wax sticks to the leaves and must be scraped off.

Because the wax must be scraped from the leaves, there are many impurities in it, making it harder to refine than carnauba wax.

Candelilla wax comes from Mexico. The plant that produces it is a low-growing, blue-green, leafless shrub that grows wild in arid country.

Mexican workers pull the plants and pile them high on the backs of patient donkeys.

The whole plants are then put into big vats, or tanks, of water over fires.

The water boils and the wax melts from the plants. Sometimes acid is added in the boiling to help free the wax. After a time the fire is allowed to die down, and the wax, which rises to the top of the tank, is ladled off and put into containers to cool and become solid.

There are plant parts and much dirt in this crude wax. Modern refining methods take care of this when the wax is shipped to other countries.

Candelilla wax has been used by the natives of Mexico for many generations. It is light tan in color and has a fragrant new-mown hay odor, as all vegetable waxes have.

Candelilla plants are being processed for wax in underground tanks containing boiling water

It is classed as a hard wax, but it is by no means as hard as the more important carnauba.

There are a few other plants that yield wax in limited quantities.

The bayberry is a fairly familiar one. Our early settlers boiled wax for candles off of bayberry fruit. Some candles are still made of fragrant bayberry wax. It has limited use, too, in soaps, ointments, and leather polish.

Some varieties of cotton plants, sugar cane, and a number of different palm trees produce usable wax.

Japan wax comes from the berries of varieties of sumac trees that grow in China and Japan. The berries are about the size of peas. They are dried, pounded, and separated into chaff and kernels. The waxy powder between the kernels and the outer skin of the berries is put in sacks and steamed. When the wax is melted, it is pressed from the sacks and refined.

Bayberry

INSECT WAX ❖❖❖❖

Insect wax is perhaps the most fascinating to us. The way it is made by insects is a marvel almost beyond human understanding. This is why the bee was a sacred insect to the early Egyptians and to many other peoples of thousands of years ago.

The bee was a symbol in the ancient hieroglyphics of Egypt thirty-five hundred years before Christ. Bees and honey and wax are referred to in the old writings of Greece, Babylonia, China, India, the Hebrews and Mohammedans, the Romans, the English, the Aztecs, and the Mayan Indians. The Bible also frequently speaks of bees and honey.

Cave men knew the sweetness of honey. In all parts of the world bees have always provided food in the form of honey, and they have fertilized flowers for countless centuries. Beeswax played an important part in man's development of the use of metal.

Strange tales and superstitions have grown up about bees. One superstition that is worldwide is called "telling the bees." Those who believe in it think that all events of family importance—deaths, births, weddings, and important plans—must be told to the bees. If they are not, bad luck will follow. When a person dies, another family member takes the key to the dead person's house and raps on the beehive with the key. Then he tells of the death.

If a birth is told about, the beehive is decorated with a strip of bright cloth.

Aristotle studied bees through a glass window in a hive he built

Another superstition is that if bees are not told of their master's death they will fly away in search of his soul.

A legend tells that bees were created from the tears of Christ on the cross.

In early times, before the life of the bee was understood, bees and their wax were believed to have mysterious powers. Bees were thought to come from the bodies of dead animals. Now we know that bees do not go near dead animals.

Aristotle, a great teacher and thinker who lived more than three hundred years before Christ, wanted to find out how bees lived and worked. He built a hive with a glass window in it so he could watch them. But the bees covered the glass with wax so that he could not see.

Honey bees make wax only when it is needed for building cells to hold honey, or when the cells are full and must be capped over with wax. To make wax the worker bees must eat honey. Scientists now believe that between seven and fifteen pounds of honey must be eaten by bees to make one pound of wax.

When worker bees have had honey in their stomachs for some time, their bodies begin to manufacture wax. Under the bee's abdomen are eight little sections that overlap like shingles. Under each section is a wax gland from which come pearly disks of wax.

The worker bee scrapes the wax scales off by scraping and catching them with spines on one hind leg. Then, while it stands on three legs, it transfers the wax to the front legs and chews and works the wax until it is soft. The bee

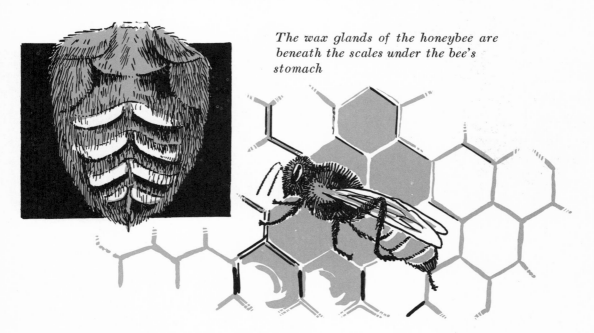

The wax glands of the honeybee are beneath the scales under the bee's stomach

uses the wax to build and shape wonderful six-sided wax cells that fit each other exactly. Some cells hold honey; others are used by the queen bee. She lays eggs in them.

The wax is separated from the honey by machines which whirl the honeycomb, throwing the liquid honey free of the wax comb. Then the wax is washed and melted. When it cools, it is formed into cakes. In factories, steam and filters are used to refine the wax.

Beeswax varies in color, depending on the kind of flowers from which the bees gathered pollen, the age of the honey, and the care given the hive. It can be whitened

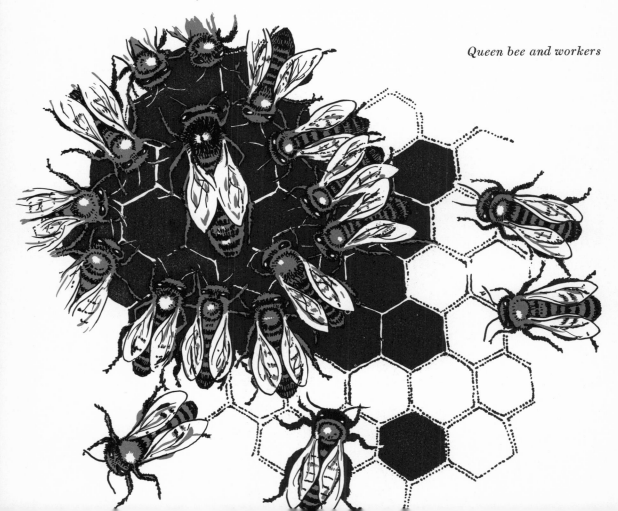

Queen bee and workers

by placing thin chips of it in sunshine and allowing the sun to bleach it. It can be bleached by chemicals, too.

Female Chinese wax insect

The United States produces millions of pounds of beeswax every year, but we do not have enough for our beeswax-using industries, so we import millions of pounds more from other countries.

Bees are not the only insects that produce wax. A number of insects do this, but not in quantities great enough to make them profitable to man. Among wax-producing insects are the cochineal insects, and many members of the family of white flies.

In China, though, millions and millions of very small insects crawl out of egg cases, attach themselves to the bark of ash trees and begin sucking the juices from the trees. Inside the tiny bodies the tree juice changes to wax which works its way outside and is built up into scales, covering the insects and merging with the wax of their close neighbors.

The wax covers the limbs of the trees in a sparkling white layer that grows to a quarter of an inch in thickness. When the warm season ends, men scrape the layers of wax from the trees, melt it so that the trapped insects and dirt settle out, and skim it. Then it is poured into molds where it hardens into Chinese wax.

Chinese insect wax has been used in China for centuries. The Chinese have long believed it to be wonderful as

Ash tree covered with wax from Chinese wax insects

medicine, and have used it for all kinds of cures. Now one of its most important uses is for candles.

In India, the lac insect, a cousin of the Chinese wax insect, works in much the same way to make a hard crust of resin, called lac, that is used for shellac. The lac is scraped from the branches of the trees where the insects are, and is refined and treated to make shellac and also a red dyestuff that comes from the lac. Shellac contains a small amount of wax, which is extracted by filtering and is known as shellac wax.

Wonderful stories have been written about whales and the whaling industry. Excitement, danger, and courage are in every one. Courage is necessary for the capture of the great mammals that churn the ocean with their mighty strength.

Whaling has been an organized industry for a thousand years. Sailing ships used to roam the seas in search of spouting jets of water that told of the whale's presence. When the watching men saw the water spouting as air came from the whale's breathing hole they cried, "Thar she blows! Thar she blows!" Then men in small boats left the mother ship and rowed desperately to get into a good position from which they could throw their harpoons into the big body. Those were dangerous times, but the prize of the whale, with all the oil and whalebone that could be taken from it, was worth the risk to the whalers.

Today whaling boats still roam the seas for whales. But now the harpoons are shot by guns, and the big ships are floating factories, where every part of the big animals can be made into useful products.

It is from the sperm whale that the valuable spermaceti wax comes. Sperm whales have large heads, making up a third of the whale's body. The front of the head is broad, and the mouth is placed at the bottom, under the head. Above the jaws, and taking up half of the head space, is a huge case or tank, filled with sperm oil. A thick layer of muscles protects the case at the top.

Whaling boats still roam the seas for sperm whales,

Large bull whales yield as much as from three to four thousand pounds of oil from the head case. This oil is a fragrant, clear, amber-colored liquid at first, but when it is allowed to stand, white crystals of spermaceti wax form in it. Strangely, the crystals are very similar to those of the wax of the little Chinese wax insects. The wax is pressed from the oil in refineries.

The white spermaceti wax makes beautiful candles that burn with a clear white light. Perhaps you have heard of candle power. This term is a measurement of the amount, or brightness, of light. It was established by the

which yield a fragrant oil that crystallizes into wax

British in London in 1860. By this measure one standard candle is the amount of light given off by a spermaceti candle that weighs one-sixth of a pound, burning at the rate of 120 grains per hour. Such a candle is seven-eighths of an inch thick.

Another animal wax is lanolin, also known as wool wax. Lanolin is a greasy wax that is widely used in salves, ointments, and cosmetics, where it is of great value. It is easily absorbed by the skin and it mixes readily with many other ingredients. Lanolin is made from the greasy coating of sheep's wool and is extracted when the wool is being cleaned for use in fabrics.

Synthetic Wax ✦✦✦✦

Man, with his knowledge of chemicals, has successfully competed with nature in the making of waxes. Man-made waxes are called synthetic waxes.

Synthetic waxes can be controlled during manufacture so that the finished product is always uniform. The amount of sunshine and rain a plant receives while growing makes a difference in plant products. Scientists can always put together exactly the same amounts of chemicals, so synthetic waxes do not vary in such things as hardness and melting temperature as natural waxes do.

Although millions of pounds of man-made wax are produced in our country each year, the cost of producing synthetic wax is much higher than the cost of harvesting and preparing natural wax. Nevertheless, more synthetic waxes are constantly being produced. Much study is going into their development and manufacture.

In general, synthetic wax is used in the same ways as natural waxes are.

Wax For the Future ✦✦✦✦

Because the quantity of natural wax produced each year is enormous, there is no possibility that men will run short of wax. There are a number of sources for more plant wax if the need arises. For example, more wax can be taken from sugarcane. Also plants such as flax, cotton, and even seaweed contain small amounts of wax, and ways can be developed for extracting it.

More wax from insects can also be secured by raising more of these small wax-producing animals.

But the wax from whales is another matter. Whales have been ruthlessly killed for their oil in the past and there was danger that they might become extinct. In 1925 the League of Nations began to study ways of protecting the "riches of the sea," which included whales, and in 1935 laws regulating the killing of whales were approved.

Now the crews of whaling ships must have licenses, and the number of whales that can be taken each year is limited. Even so, we still need to be concerned about the preservation of these huge animals of the sea.

As for mineral wax, it is not known how much of it still lies beneath the earth's surface, but there is little doubt that the supply is still very great.

We have seen that wax has been important in the development of many products that give comfort and pleasure to men. Through untold centuries its use has grown, until at present our need for it gives employment to tens of thousands of people. All over the world people are busy harvesting, transporting, refining, making, and selling wax products.

In these days we are constantly creating new scientific objects and chemical combinations, seeking to improve ways of life. So the use of wax goes on. In the future we will surely continue to find new methods of making greater use of the wonderful wax in our world.

INDEX

Africa, 15
Alfred, King, 28
America, 6–10, 29, 57
animal wax, 41, 59–61
Aristotle, 54
artists, 10, 12–14, 24–25
ash trees, 57
Austria, 42
Aztecs, 14, 53

Babylonia, 11, 53
baking, 39
batik, 21–23
bayberries, 29, 52
bees, 53–57
beeswax, 7, 11, 26, 28, 53, 55–57
beliefs, *see* superstitions
Bible, 53
Brazil, 32, 46–50

candelilla, 28, 50–52
candle power, 60–61
candles, 28–29, 46, 52, 58, 60–61
carbon paper, 31–33
carnauba wax, 32–33, 46–50
chewing gum, 40
China, 15, 28, 52, 53, 57–58
Cire Perdu, see Lost Wax
clay, 14, 15–18
cleaners, 40
cochineals, 57
cosmetics, 35, 61
crayons, 23, 40

Da Vinci, Leonardo, 13
Degas, Edgar, 13
dentistry, 35
duplicating, 31–33

Edison, Thomas, 30–31
Egypt, 10–11, 15, 19–21, 53
encaustic painting, 21
England, 28, 53; *see also* London
Europe, 29; *see also countries of*

Flaxman, John, 14
flies, white, 57
floors, 37
flowers, 34, 53
France, 28

Gainsborough, Thomas, 13

geologists, 42
Greece, 11, 20, 53

hard wax, 52
healing, 11, 58; *see also* medicine
Hebrews, 53
history, American, 6–10
honey, 53, 55–56

India, 11, 15, 53, 58
Indians, 14; *see also* tribes
inks, 25
insect wax, 28, 41, 53–58, 63

Japan wax, 52
Java, and batik, 21–23
jelly, 45
jewelry, 18

lac, wax from, 58
lamps, 26–28
lanolin, 61
lantern, 28
lanthorn, 28
lighting, methods of, 26–29
lignite, 43
lithography, 24–25
London, 5–6, 61
Lost Wax process, 15–19

machine parts, 18–19
Madame Tussaud's, 5–6, 13
marine animals, *see* animal wax
Mayans, 11, 53
medicine, 35, 58, 61
metals, 14–19, 25
Mexico, 28, 50–52
Michelangelo, 13
mineral wax, 41–45, 63
models, 5–14, 35; *see also* molds
Mohammedans, 53
molds, 14–18
montan, 41, 43
mummies, 10–11

nature, wax in, 28, 34, 62–63

oil paint, 21
ouricury wax, 50
ozokerite, 41–43

pads, magic, 40
painting, 20–24

paints, 40
palm, 28, 46–50, 52
paraffin, 29, 41, 43, 45
pencils, marking, 40
petroleum, 29, 42, 43, 45
plants, 28, 29, 34, 52, 62; *see also names of*
Pliny, 28
polish, 37
Ponce de Leon, Juan, 9
potters, 14
preservation, 34–39
printing, 23–25
protection, 34–39, 45

records, 30–31
Rome, 11, 20, 28, 53
rubber products, 37
Russia, 42

sculptors, 12–14
Senefelder, Alois, 23–24
shellac, 58
sperm wax, 29, 59–61
sumac, 52
superstitions, 10–11, 53–54
surgery, 35
synthetic wax, 62

tallow, 28, 29, 32
Texas, 42
tinfoil, 30, 31
Toltecs, 14
torches, 26
Tussaud, Madame, 5–6, 13

U. S., *see* America
USSR, *see* Russia
Utah, 42

vegetable wax, 41, 46–52
waterproofing, 21, 23–24, 37
wax, 41, 62–63, *see also* kinds of
wax museums, 5–10
wax paper, 37–38
Wedgwood, Josiah, 14
whales, 29, 59–61, 63
white flies, 57
wicks, 26–29
wool wax, 61
Wright, Patience Lovell, 13
writing, 20

Printed in U.S.A.